FOR KAY—

A BOOK OF GEMS
FOR A JEWEL,

LOVE,
Tom
VERMONT 1984

ANNIVERSARY STONES

Birthstones have been given and worn since ancient times. The earliest choice of gems was probably based on astrology, and the stones had mystical significance. Two Zodiacal lists are given. Although they come from a seventeenth century book, the first likely dates from the Middle Ages or before and the second from the sixteenth century. Dr. G. F. Kunz in *The Curious Lore of Precious Stones* summarized eight lists of various countries which date from ancient times to 1900. In 1912 the National Association of Jewelers agreed on a list which, with a few new gems added later as alternatives, is the standard followed in the United States today.

No such standard has been set suggesting a list of appropriate wedding anniversary gems. At the back of this book is a list of stones and their traditional significance. If followed, it brings a lifetime of marital happiness and lovely jewels.

ZODIACAL STONES

   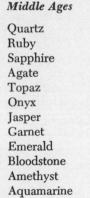 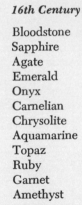

	Zodiac	*Middle Ages*	*16th Century*
ARIES	March 21-April 19	Quartz	Bloodstone
TAURUS	April 20-May 20	Ruby	Sapphire
GEMINI	May 21-June 21	Sapphire	Agate
CANCER	June 22-July 22	Agate	Emerald
LEO	July 23-Aug. 22	Topaz	Onyx
VIRGO	Aug. 23-Sept. 22	Onyx	Carnelian
LIBRA	Sept. 23-Oct. 23	Jasper	Chrysolite
SCORPIO	Oct. 24-Nov. 21	Garnet	Aquamarine
SAGITTARIUS	Nov. 22-Dec. 21	Emerald	Topaz
CAPRICORN	Dec. 22-Jan. 19	Bloodstone	Ruby
AQUARIUS	Jan. 20-Feb. 18	Amethyst	Garnet
PISCES	Feb. 19-March 20	Aquamarine	Amethyst

BIRTHSTONE LISTS

Dr. Kunz' Summary

JANUARY–Garnet; Hyacinth Zircon

FEBRUARY–Amethyst; Hyacinth Zircon; Pearl

MARCH–Jasper; Bloodstone

APRIL–Sapphire; Diamond

MAY–Agate; Emerald; Carnelian

JUNE–Emerald; Agate; Turquoise; Pearl

JULY–Onyx; Carnelian; Ruby; Turquoise

AUGUST–Carnelian; Moonstone; Topaz; Alexandrite

SEPTEMBER–Chrysolite; Sardonyx

OCTOBER–Beryl; Aquamarine; Opal

NOVEMBER–Topaz; Pearl

DECEMBER–Ruby; Turquoise; Bloodstone

Jewelers Association's List

JANUARY–Garnet

FEBRUARY–Amethyst

MARCH–Aquamarine

APRIL–Diamond

MAY–Emerald

JUNE–Pearl, Moonstone, or Alexandrite

JULY–Ruby

AUGUST–Peridot or Sardonyx

SEPTEMBER–Sapphire

OCTOBER–Opal or Tourmaline

NOVEMBER–Topaz

DECEMBER–Turquoise or Zircon

Enjoying Gems

Enjoying Gems

THE LURE AND LORE OF JEWEL STONES

By ROBERT WYNDHAM

ILLUSTRATIONS BY ROBERT MACLEAN

THE STEPHEN GREENE PRESS, BRATTLEBORO, VT.

This book has been produced in the United States of America: designed by R. L. Dothard Associates, composed and printed by Vermont Printing Company, and bound by Robert Burlen & Son.

It is published by the Stephen Greene Press, Brattleboro, Vermont 05301.

Library of Congress Catalog Card Number: 72-173403
International Standard Book Number: 0-8289-0145-7

An ancient legend tells that the Devil prized his wife above all his worldly possessions, and kept her locked in a magnificent palace he designed like a great jewel box constructed of every beautiful gem stone on earth.

Now, I prize my wife in the same way, but never possessed the power to fashion so grand a castle or even keep her locked up. So, I built this book with words about joyful gems and dedicate it to my Genia.

ROBERT WYNDHAM

Morristown, New Jersey

Contents

THE ALLURE OF GEMS

Be a gem watcher and you will become a gem wearer, for a whole new world of beauty will open for you if you will look at gems and learn a little about them. This world of gems might be compared to that of art. Although it is wonderful if you can, it is not necessary to own a jewel or a painting to enjoy it. Nor is it necessary to become an expert with great technical knowledge, a mineralogist or gemmologist. The amateur gem watcher and art lover alike, thrilling to his new discovery, will find that even the finest masterpieces of nature and the arts are available for his pleasure.

Art museums and museums of natural history display collections of precious stones that date from ancient times. They can be seen at no cost or for a small fee. Some museums show the rough, uncut mineral rocks from which gems are taken; others show cut and polished jewels unmounted or jewels set in rings, bracelets, brooches, necklaces, and earrings. And every jewelry store offers a free display of gems.

There is another close analogy between aficionados of art and of gem stones. The former may purchase inexpensive paintings, figurines, or reproductions they admire, fitting the expenditure to their means. The latter may do the same with jewels, for some of the loveliest and most colorful gems, or their synthetic equivalents, can be purchased at surprisingly low cost. But the gem buyer should know how to look for what he can afford.

The average person is usually familiar only with the few high-priced gems that are in great popular demand, and often it is popularity and demand alone which keep jewel stones in the expensive category. In the past, some stones have risen to wide popularity and demand, consequently becoming highly priced, only to fall again. Although they are no longer in demand and are little known today, they are very likely to rise again in the future. Other elements also influence cost, and these will be discussed later.

There are many misconceptions about gems. For example, far too much emphasis has been placed on hardness. It is common knowledge that the diamond is the hardest stone; it resists wear, that is, scratching or being scratched. But even a diamond can be chipped or cracked by carelessness. No gem, hard or soft, should be worn while the wearer is washing dishes, doing plumbing or carpentry or digging and pruning in the garden or orchard.

An outstanding illustration of the misconception relating hardness to value and durability is that a fine emerald, carat for carat, is worth two or three times more than a diamond, and yet that beautiful green stone is not rated nearly as hard. Jewelry experts say that some of the ancient emeralds of Cleopatra, cut down and reset, still exist somewhere in the world. Many articles of jewelry found in ancient Egyptian tombs of 3500-2500 B.C. contain a variety of ornamental materials —amethyst and carnelian, even colored glass—which are nowhere nearly as hard as diamond. Since these have lasted 5,000 years, the importance of "hardness" in evaluating gems is seen as a matter of perspective. If properly cared for, the softest gem stones will last for many generations.

It is sometimes surprising to learn that other gems are equal to or of greater value than diamonds, and to learn—as we shall later—how and why diamond price is maintained. Another common misconception concerns the importance of the characteristic colors of the various gems. For example, the garnet, commonly thought of as a red jewel, is found in an extremely costly green variety.

Just as it is not essential to know the technical details of how Rembrandt crafted his colors—the minerals and dyes he used, and their chemical formulas—to appreciate his paintings, it is not essential to know the technical aspects of gems to appreciate them. There will be those, however, who do want to know more about the mineralogy and sources of gems. There is a fascination in such knowledge, and such terms as *chromatic dispersion* and *crystalline form* are charming conversation pieces! It is possible for gem fanciers to become interested in chatoyancy, electrical properties, geometric optics, cutting, faceting, polishing, mounting and design, single or double refraction, fluorescence, cleavage and chemical formulas, but these aspects are highly technical and, if they do not appeal to a gem watcher, they can be left to a jeweler. A list of more technical books is given in the bibliography. This book is intended only as an introduction to the world of beautiful gems.

Alexandrite

This little-known but remarkable jewel is a changeling. It shows green by daylight and red under artificial light. The finest, clearly transparent specimens of alexandrite are very seldom above four to five carats, and usually they are much smaller. The precise shade of the red or the green in these rare gems can be described in various ways depending on the impression of the individual looking at them. For example, the green may be described as emerald, grass, splendid, or elegant, while the red may be described as ruby, columbine, garnet, raspberry, or fiery.

A genuine, top-quality alexandrite is an expensive gem and extremely hard to find. In 1970 the author learned that a New York dealer had only two fine alexandrites in stock. One was slightly over four and three-quarters carats, selling for $14,500 and the other smaller one was $5,000.

Fortunately, specimens of alexandrite are not quite so uncommon in the translucent, less-clear class. These occur in larger sizes than the rare clear stones and are not nearly so costly, their value depending upon the degree of translucence (amount of light able to pass through the stone), the number of or lack of flaws, the weight in carats, and the colors.

As with the transparent specimens of alexandrite, observers give varying descriptions of the colors of the translucent alexandrites. The daylight green may be seen as dull-grass, grayish, opaque, olive, or elm-leaf. The red may seem murky, cinnamon, Venetian, dull coral, or brownish. All may be correct, for the gems are found in a fairly wide range of colors. As the degree of translucence approaches the opaque, there is less fire and color from within, and the value drops.

The story of the discovery of alexandrite is an interesting one. In the 1830's some miners were working along the face of a rocky hill in the Ural Mountains at a location where emeralds were found. One man gathered some stones which looked like emeralds and took them back to the camp after the workday was over. But strangely, in the light of the campfire that night the stones shone red! When morning came and the stones showed green again in the daylight, the miners realized they had found a new and mysterious gem.

When the stones were taken back to civilization, they were examined carefully. In 1839 they were identified and named for the heir apparent to the Russian throne, who later ruled as Tzar Alexander II. The alexandrite was always especially popular in Russia because its green and red were the Imperial colors.

Most jewels belong to a mineral "family" and have brothers and sisters. The family name of the alexandrite is chrysoberyl, and a famous child of that family is the genuine cat's-eye, which will be

discussed in a later section. Another child is yellow chrysoberyl. This beautiful chartreuse yellow gem is sometimes miscalled chrysolite, which is from another mineral family. The word *chrysoberyl* comes from the Greek and means golden beryl, while *chrysolite*, from the same source, means golden stone. It would seem that the Greeks did not know of alexandrite—or they would have had a word for it.

One of the finest examples of the true yellow chrysoberyl is a large, cut stone (over seventy-four carats) in the American Museum of Natural History in New York. As with kunzites (also discussed later) and some diamonds, such as the yellow and the pink, alexandrites are seldom to be seen in public or private displays.

Despite the fact that our knowledge of alexandrite dates only from its discovery in the 1830's, it is entirely possible that the gem was found earlier in history, but that its mysterious changeling quality seemed devil-magic to superstitious ancient peoples. It may have been taboo to have one or speak of it. Perhaps they threw such stones away in a river or lake to keep their discovery secret. At any rate, no description fitting alexandrite has ever been found in the older literatures.

Legends about alexandrite are rare because of its short history. Although it may have been thought of as evil in the past, since its discovery it has always been considered a good-luck stone in Russia. Whatever its magical powers, it is a beautiful and durable gem, and it will be your good fortune if you have a chance to enjoy one.

Amethyst

The royal violet color and the delicate fire of the amethyst have made it one of the most admired of all gems. That it was popular in ancient times is shown by the number of legends about it that have come down through the ages in many lands. The true amethyst is a jewel of fabulous beauty.

That word *true* is important. The amethyst is a member of the large quartz family, which will be discussed in a later section. It is easier to recognize the true amethyst color than to describe it. But deep violet, royal purple, or rich violet would be close.

An amethyst may be lavender, pale violet, or pinkish-blue. It can also be very dark purple. All are lovely gems, but the rarer and more valuable amethyst must be of a certain true color which a jeweler can best distinguish from others.

Along with all the legends, superstitions, and stories about the amethyst, there remains a fascinating mystery. What gives the amethyst its color? This question, not as yet resolved by experts to the satisfaction and agreement of all, involves technicalities (in chemistry and geometric optics), so discussion is avoided here. But you might set out to solve the mystery, and derive great pleasure in doing so!

Amethyst is the birthstone now generally assigned to February, but this was not always so. In many countries at various times in history the gem was associated with different astrological signs which were supposed to guide the destinies of those born under them—a confusing situation true of all gems. Disagreement about birthstone gems was finally settled, at least here in the United States, in 1912, when a standard table was set up that took into account all the world lore associated with birthstones.

Still, our accepted birthstone table doesn't agree entirely with those of many people here and in other nations, especially those who follow astrology faithfully.

The Greeks had words for everything and amethyst could have come from several. *Amenthos* might be translated "not to be drunk" and *amethystos* as "remedy for drunkenness." At any rate, the magic of the gem has traditionally been associated with protection against inebriation.

A completely unrelated tradition is the frequent use of amethyst in ecclesiastical rings, especially those of bishops. The gem has been given many attributes and they are all good. A *few* of its powers are: controls evil thoughts; calms evil passions; quickens intelligence; makes a man shrewd in business; preserves soldiers

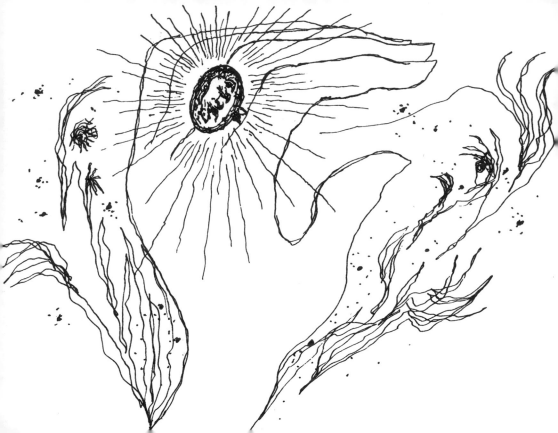

from battle wounds; aids the warrior to victory; helps the hunter in search of game; protects the wearer from contagious diseases; and puts demons to flight if the figure of a bear is inscribed on the jewel. Anyone can see that the amethyst is not only beautiful but powerful!

In Oriental beliefs, however, there was a qualification which stated that most of those good powers were properties of only the *perfect* gems. It was thought that any flaw or imperfection in color (in this, or any gem) would absolutely counteract the powers of the amethyst, and in fact work in *reverse*. You are warned.

There are a number of Biblical references to the amethyst. It was one of the twelve precious stones in the high priest Aaron's breastplate. The twelfth foundation of the Holy City was built of amethyst. The Jews believed that the amethyst could induce dreams and visions, and here is a curious analogy to hypnosis, for it is now well known that staring long enough at an object reflecting varying light may produce hypnosis. Even the colors of amethyst are right; French psychiatrist Dr. Paul Ferenz, in 1906, recommended a violet-blue disk, rotated before the eyes, as an aid to hypnosis.

There is a charming old French narrative poem which slightly alters a more ancient Greek legend about the nymph named Amethyst. While passing through a forest she was set upon by the tigers of Bacchus, the god of wine. Amethyst called out for help and the goddess Diana miraculously changed her into a statue of white stone. At this Bacchus suffered qualms of conscience, and for some reason poured wine over the statue, giving the stone that beautiful purple color we call amethyst.

For some time true amethyst was valued equally with the diamond; then great finds in South America and elsewhere made amethyst more plentiful. As its rarity decreased, so did its price. Now the supply of fine amethysts has once more begun to diminish (as the mines are worked out), and the cost will probably increase again, for the demand is constant. An amethyst of the finest color and crystal perfection is one of nature's masterpieces.

Aquamarine

The clear blue aquamarine is a valued gem of ancient lineage. The name means sea water and, as with the amethyst, descriptions of its color vary. It may be described as greenish-blue, limpid blue-green, or crystal blue. The gem actually does occur in varied shades and clarity, but only one special color is the rarest and therefore the most highly prized. The stone cannot be too pale or too green, for it's the precise blue color that makes a fine aquamarine rare and precious.

All "aquas" are a pleasure to behold, rare or not. A varied display of them is like seeing the many colors of the oceans and lakes around the world. One is the color of the Atlantic on a calm day at noon off New Hampshire; another is the color of the Mediterranean in the morning, or Lake Killarney. Every aquamarine recalls a similar hue or tint of some body of water you have enjoyed. And many of the legends about these stones and the magic qualities attributed to them quite naturally relate to marine subjects.

The aquamarine is of the beryl family, along with four other children. Surprisingly the emerald is one, along with the goshenite, the morganite, and the golden beryl. The goshenite is utterly clear and shows no color. Golden beryl is as named. A morganite is a fine pink color. The colors of emerald and aqua you know. Chrysoberyls like alexandrite and cat's-eye are close cousins of the beryls, though the addition of a little silicon makes them heavier.

The color of beryl stones, like that of amethyst, is a mystery, as experts disagree on exactly what substances provide the colorations. Emeralds vary in hue and depth of color, as do aquamarines. Some morganites are so pale a pink that they might be called goshenite; the color golden beryl is no one specific yellow, but varies.

The Sumerians, Egyptians, and Hebrews admired and valued aquamarine greatly. It was a symbol of happiness and everlasting youth, also a very lucky talisman for sailors, or anyone taking a voyage over water, fresh or salt. The Greeks and Romans prized the aquamarine for these reasons, and the Romans believed that if the figure of a frog were carved on an aqua, it served to reconcile enemies and make them friends.

In the Christian era the aquamarine was identified with the Apostle, St. Thomas, because it "imitated the sea and the air," and the Saint "made long journeys by sea, even to India, to preach salvation." Identifying a certain jewel with one of the twelve apostles was a common practice. In earlier days one gem was assigned to each of the twelve tribes of Israel. The number twelve was powerful in ancient times. There were twelve jewel stones in Aaron's breastplate, twelve gem stones forming the twelve foundations of the Holy City, and gems were assigned to each of the twelve signs of the zodiac.

William Langland's *The Vision concerning Piers the Plowman* (second version about 1377) mentions the aquamarine as an antidote for poison. This antidote was undoubtedly known throughout Europe, and as there was a considerable amount of royalty-poisoning taking place in those times, the gem must have been in great demand for that purpose alone! It wasn't necessary to pulverize the stone and munch on it; it was effective just worn as a pendant or in a ring.

Specimens of choice aquamarine are fairly common among gem displays in museums, and their wide price range makes them available to almost everyone.

Cat's-Eye

Gems that resemble the eyes of cats have fascinated people since before history began. There is also a jewel stone that looks like a hawk's eye, but it has never been as popular.

The true and most valuable cat's-eye gems are from the mineral family chrysoberyl. These are rare and costly and held in great esteem in Oriental countries, where most of them are to be found today.

Then there are some rare cat's-eye specimens occurring now and then in aquamarines, morganite, yellow beryl, garnet, and tourmaline stones. But the quartz family, with its many gem children, produces many of the lower-cost cat's-eyes, tigereyes and hawk's-eyes. These are the ones seen most often in nature.

These attractive "eye" stones are always cut or fashioned with a rounded high dome rather than with a flat top or sharp facets. This method, the "cabochon" cut, allows the stone to catch more light and brings out the eye effect better.

Cat's-eyes show the basic colors from gold, to greenish-yellow, green, even reddish- to dark-brown. The "eye" slit or line is generally lighter, almost white in gems of basic lighter shades, and more bluish in stones of darker shades. The more expensive stones show more fire and glow more strongly than most of the quartz "eyes," and the stripe is better defined.

The tigereye is of the quartz family, and ranges in basic color from yellow-browns to ruddy dark brown and black. The hawk's-eyes, also of the quartz family, are grayish-blue, like the eyes of the bird itself.

Only in a museum or gallery is it possible to see the many colors and shades of the "eye" stones, and the wide variety of combinations in which they are found.

A jeweler can explain what gives the stones their unusual visual effects. An eye in a gem that seems to move when the stone is turned *needs* explanation.

In the United States "eye" stones were very popular from about 1840 to 1920, when their fashion waned. Men wore them in rings, tie stickpins, cuff links, and watchchain charms. Women wore them in brooches, pendants, and bar pins. When some of these mountings went out of fashion, so did the demand for cat's-eyes in rings.

The "eye" stones are reputed to bring excellent luck to the wearer. Most Oriental writers specify Thursday as the day a genuine cat's-eye brings the greatest luck, although a few argue it is more effective on Wednesday. Cat's-eyes, in addition to bringing good luck, counteract the bad luck associated with the number thirteen or a multiple of it. For example, they are great luck charms for thirteenth, twenty-sixth, and thirty-ninth birthdays. They are good warners, as well. To dream of a live cat's eyes means one should beware of treachery or deceit. Wearing the stone guards against such misfortune. In Ceylon the stone is thought to be the abode of a helpful genii. Also, wearing a cat's-eye is said to ward off tears of sorrow, to shield one from evil spells, and to relieve croup and asthma. These are only a few of the magic powers cat's-eyes possess.

Hindu poets describe a Kalpa tree as a glowing mass of beautiful gems. Its roots were of one kind of gem stones, the trunk of several other kinds, while its branches were laden with all sorts of jewels. Cat's-eyes were in the uppermost part. Wonderful trees such as this, bearing precious gems of various kinds, occur in legends of many lands. In Chinese, Sanskrit, Arabic and Burmese literatures the gem is listed as one of the nine most valuable in astrology and the occult sciences. Lastly, cat's-eyes are reputed to be protection against financial ruin. So there you have it. No matter what you spend for one, you are sure of a fascinating, beautiful stone and a good investment.

Diamond

Diamond is the hardest known substance on earth and the commercial, nongem or lower quality diamonds, are used directly or indirectly in almost every industry and business throughout the world.

Diamonds occur in nature in many qualities, and over eighty-seven percent of all that are mined or found each year are used in industry. Even so, the remaining stones of gem quality amount to about half a ton, or approximately three million carats!

Diamonds occur in all colors and vary in shade from yellow to pink, red, green, blue, brown, and even black; however, the most valuable of all diamonds is the clear, or colorless, variety. This is correctly called the "white" diamond and incorrectly "blue-white." All others are called by their own color—such as "yellow diamond" or "blue" or "pink"—so there is no confusion about the children's names in this mineral family. Diamonds also can be transparent, translucent, and opaque; but only the transparent ones are of gem value.

In all gem stones, flaws occur more commonly in the larger sizes. Diamonds are no exception. Diamonds below three carats down to the half-carat sizes in general are only *almost* perfect. The cost jumps about two times from one-half to one carat, and again going up to two carats. The larger rough gem diamond is expertly cut and faceted to eliminate pits, cracks, and discolorations. Gem fanciers usually see only the smaller examples unless they attend public exhibits of large and rare specimens.

The flashing fire and the dazzling lights of a fine diamond that has been cut and polished by an expert show well what beauty can be achieved when nature's creation is coupled with man's art. Oddly enough, in its original "found" condition the diamond is seldom a thing of beauty, as it may be covered with extraneous cloudy materials. But, after expert cutters and polishers work on it, you have what is generally called the King of Gems.

The extreme hardness of the diamond renders it almost immune to outside surface wear (abrasion and scratching) or wear from the clasps of its mountings (settings). In great demand, it maintains a fairly constant value and is a convenient form of wealth—easily converted into cash—easy to carry and to hide.

Reasons for the diamond's stability in value are given in some of the books listed in the bibliography. But basically, the mining of diamond gems is tied so closely to the commercial type that there must be some sort of control. In big production years some of the diamonds that are mined are stored away to maintain a supply for the lean years in which the demand is heavy. Otherwise industries all over the world would suffer and perhaps fail. In times of war, it is the control of gem release that is first relaxed, while the industrial diamond industry continues under rigid control. A vast world-wide combine, presides over this rather benevolent cartel, controlling about ninety-five percent of the diamond market and keeping prices fairly constant.

The diamond is really a fairly new gem as we know it today. It is mentioned often in tales from previous civilizations, but it was frequently misnamed or confused with other clear stones that were also hard and sparkling.

No one knew how to cut or facet this hardest of all minerals until four or five hundred years ago, and in ancient times any and all hard, colorless gems such as sapphire, topaz, zircon, and beryl were often called diamonds. Even clear crystal quartz, though not as hard, was confused with the King. Adamas, adamant, diamant, and other supposed diamonds were often misnamed, in all the literatures.

Diamonds were mined at a number of places in India a long time ago, but they were marketed in a town called Golconda, so that name, in all lands, became associated with any place or source of fabulous wealth, including gold mines. After that, Brazilian "finds" in 1725 produced so many diamonds that, despite some price control, the world price fell. When

diamonds were found in great quantities in Africa in the 1870's, world-wide control was organized.

Diamonds vary in hardness and they also vary in fire, some having a dull surface luster as if they were dimmed slightly by a thin film of oil. A real diamond expert can tell with some certainty where a diamond comes from by those and other differences, including the colors.

For diamond aficionados there are public displays in many places. The blue Hope diamond (some describe it "green-tint blue") can be seen in Washington, D.C., at the Smithsonian Institution. The marvelous Tiffany canary yellow diamond (sometimes called "orange-yellow") is on display at Tiffany's in New York. Any jeweler has diamonds in smaller sizes, the smallest of which are used in clusters or in jewelry pieces with other stones.

Famous diamonds have true histories that far outstrip fiction. Only two will be touched on here; for information on the rest, such as the Orlov, Dresden, Regent or Pitt, Cullinan, Great Mogul, and Koh-i-nur, see some of the books listed in the bibliography.

The forty-four carat blue Hope diamond is reputed to carry bad luck. Marie Antoinette wore it once, and was, of course, executed; the sultana of Abdul Hamid was shot by her husband while wearing it; and another owner was drowned at sea. The stone known as the Paul I of Russia has an interesting thread woven through its story: It is a *ruby-red* diamond. There was a *Red Revolution*.

It is now shown in museums in Red Russia.

Marie Antoinette was supposed to have bought a diamond necklace of 2,800 carats, one of the greatest ever known. Its cost, contrasted with the poverty of some of the Paris population, was influential in bringing about the French Revolution.

The diamond has been considered a bringer of victory and an emblem of fearlessness and invincibility; it is said to drive away ghosts if worn on the left arm; and, around 1585 it was called the gem of reconciliation, as it enhanced the love of a husband for his wife.

Hindu writers claimed that if perfect diamonds were offered to the gods, the donor could attain Nirvana. Some sixteenth-century experts said a diamond would glow as long as the wearer was virtuous, but if the wearer sinned, the stone would grow dim. A diamond is also reputed a protection against poison, and a bringer of good fortune. And some have said it can make the wearer invisible!

When buying a diamond, consult your local jeweler, who has the equipment with which to examine and choose the finest stones for you.

Emerald

The true emerald belongs to the beryl mineral family mentioned in the section on aquamarines. Carat for carat, a fine emerald may be two or three times as valuable as a fine diamond. A flawless, clear emerald of the right shade is very rare and is usually found in only small sizes. There are far fewer fine large emeralds in the world than fine large diamonds. Most large emeralds have cracks and flaws, or are cloudy or off-color. So you'll have to content yourself with just viewing the few large, fine specimens on display, although it is financially possible to own a reasonably small one.

That word "true" is always a guidepost. In ancient times many gem stones were mistakenly called emeralds just because they were green. Today there are six or seven gem stones, each beautifully green and valuable, called this or that kind of emerald. All that is necessary to know is that the stone is of the beryl mineral family and is called "emerald"—with no qualifying name in front of it. A tag or label such as "evening" emerald or "morning" emerald indicates some *other* gem stone. When a green jewel is called a "cape" emerald, or "lithium" emerald—it isn't; there is only "emerald."

As with most gem stones, a large ways of describing the color of a perfect emerald. Some say it is clear rich grass-green; or limpid, velvety grass-green; or perhaps deep transparent green with a vitreous luster. However, as with other gems, after having seen a number of stones of the "perfect" color and clarity, it is easy to recognize one that is just a little "off"—perhaps too pale, too close to bluish-green, or murky dark green. Yet, as with other gems, some people actually prefer the off shades. This is a matter of individual choice. One collector of precious gems considers "white" dia-monds insipid, and only admires diamonds of color.

The emerald is mentioned with deep admiration and reverence in the literatures of all nations. The Sumerians said if one was worn in a ring on the little finger of the left hand it would cure inflammations of the eyes. Moreover, there were reports in every language of the beneficial effect of emeralds on the eyes. Some said they cured eye troubles if worn, while others said that the curative effect came from gazing deeply into the green gem for a while.

Both King Solomon and Cleopatra were said to have owned emerald mines. The latter's mines turned out a great many of these stones, and a number of museums in the world display emerald

beads and scarabs that came from them around 2,000 years ago. This destroys the notion that gem stones not rated as very hard are not durable. Emeralds, and other fine gems, are not in the same hardness rank with diamonds, but they manage to last well. True, they will scratch more easily, but scratches can be polished off.

In China, Thursday was the day for wearing green raiment, and of course emeralds. On the other hand, various countries of the East and the West differed on which day the emerald brought good luck. Some seers said Monday; some said Tuesday; others insisted that Friday was the day.

Many famous people throughout history have worn emeralds: Alexander the Great had a very large one set in his girdle; Charlemagne's crown and other royal equipment contained a number of them; and Henry II, when he was made King of Ireland in 1171, was given a large emerald ring.

It is said that just a flash of an emerald will kill a poisonous snake. But Cleopatra, for all her emeralds, died from the bite of the poisonous asp. Ptolemy, King of Egypt at the time, had an emerald engraved with the portrait of Lucullus, the great Roman general, and presented it to him when the latter visited the land of the Nile in the first century B.C.

The Spanish conquistadores seized an immense fortune in emeralds when they conquered Peru, South America, and Mexico in the 1500's. The Bible mentions that the fourth foundation of New Jerusalem was of emerald. Paracelsus recommended emerald ground up with laudanum, an opium derivative, as a medicine for certain fevers and ills. The accounts and legends of this gem stone throughout history would form a book in themselves.

The word "emerald" is from the Sanskrit, although many changes have been made in it. It always seems to have meant green, however. In various languages it was stated that an emerald enables one to foretell future events—if gazed into, if put under the tongue, if worn on the left side, or on the left hand. Emeralds were also believed to reveal what was true or false and said to be the sure antidote for enchantments and spells. They were also to give eloquence in speech and make people not only more intelligent but *honest*.

Garnet

Nearly everyone thinks of garnet as a red gem, but some jewels in this family range in color from pale orange to dark red and violet. Garnet can also range from cinnamon to brown and from olive to green. Moreover, a flawless clear green garnet (the demantoid variety) is one of the most beautiful and costly gems in existence. A fine demantoid of five carats is even rarer than a choice emerald in that size, and its dispersion or fire is higher than that of a diamond, but this brilliance is somewhat masked by the color, so a white (clear) diamond shows more fire to the eye.

The garnet has been a popular gem throughout history. Some garnets were found as beads in a necklace (worn by a young man) in an Egyptian grave dating back to 3500 B.C. This bears out what has already been said about the hardness and lasting qualities of gem stones. Garnets rank well below diamonds in hardness, and varieties of garnets differ among themselves in this regard. But given a chance, they last a long time.

To avoid confusion we will consider only three kinds of garnets here: the green *demantoid*, already mentioned; the more common red variety, the *pyrope*; and a more valuable, deeper red variety, the *almandine*. The almandine garnet was often called a "carbuncle" in old writings. This was the stone that was said to have provided the light in Noah's Ark during those wet, dark days and nights.

As with most gem stones, a large clear garnet is a rarity. The larger gems are usually flawed, cracked, or of poor or mixed color. Several fine large specimens are said to be in Vienna and Dresden museums, and the King of Saxony is reported to have had a garnet of over 465 carats.

The almandine garnet sometimes comes in a four-ray star stone, but very rarely in the six-ray specimen. Plato had his portrait engraved on an almandine garnet by a Roman engraver, and this likeness happens to be one of the best that remains of him.

The pyrope garnet is seen most often, because it is the most common variety found in nature. It occurs in generous quantities in various parts of the world, even in small sand particles on many beaches, as well as in rock formations in many places. It has been said that anyone, even if he has poor eyesight, can find a piece or two of garnet on a casual field trip. The same is said of several other gem stones—quartz and feldspar—which also occur frequently on earth.

Bohemia (now part of Czechoslovakia) was once noted as a tremendous source of garnet, and at one time cutting, polishing, and mounting garnets was a very rich industry in that country. A number of Bohemian castles and churches had magnificent interior decorations of garnet. The Anglo-Saxons were also fond of the

stone, and their jewelry was set with garnets mounted in many forms.

The name for this gem stone comes from the Latin word for pomegranate, which seems logical because small garnet crystals look like pomegranate seeds. The pomegranate was a favorite in Old Spain and so was the garnet. In Spanish astrology the garnet once represented the sun.

There are ancient traditions and legends about the garnet, and magic powers have been attributed to it. Some Hebrew writers include it as one of the twelve gems in Aaron's breastplate. Christian tradition long considered the blood-red garnet as symbolic of Christ's sacrifice. The Koran holds that it illuminates the Fourth Heaven of the Moslems. The Greeks said it guarded children from drowning. Like other gems, it was said to be potent against poison and also against bad dreams.

There are some authorities who claim that a garnet engraved with the figure of a lion is a really all-round effective charm. Then too, it is said to prevent incontinence, preserve honor and health, cure all diseases, and protect travelers. But even without a carved Simba, the garnet is considered a remedy for profuse bleeding and inflammatory diseases.

Still, you should use a little care in how much you look at a garnet, for it is thought to stimulate the heart. This can lead to passion, anger, even apoplexy. And though it is able to cheer you up, it can excite you too much and bring on insomnia. One writer said that if it loses its luster and shine it is a sure sign of coming disaster.

Jade

For thousands of years jade has been a revered gem stone in China and in many other countries. The Chinese, Mayas, Aztecs, and the Maoris of New Zealand have long valued it for use in jewelry and in carvings of sacred religious figures. Even before there were written records of it, this tough, strong stone was used for axe heads, spear points, daggers, and sacred knives in pagan religious ceremonies.

Many volumes have been written on jade, and any complete study of it in-volves a knowledge of antiques, history, religion, and archaeology. Thus jade can be touched on only lightly here, and only as a gem. Some of the books in the bibliography give more detailed information.

There are two distinct stones known as jade—jadeite and nephrite. Both are fairly hard and extremely tough (or strong). It is difficult for the layman to tell them apart. Also, as with almost every gem stone, when they are free of coloration chemicals, both types are white. When nature's various chemical

colorations are present, both jadeite and nephrite range from shades of green, to blue, yellow, red, lavender, gray, and black. Jades (nephrite and jadeite) are never completely transparent, but the closer the stones come to being translucent, the more value they have, if the color is right.

Dealers in jade have stated that very fine, almost transparent white jade can equal a diamond in value, carat for carat. Then there are collectors of the beautiful green jade, almost emerald in color, who prize it, along with the fine blue jade, as the equal of any precious jewel stone.

The value collectors place on jade varies greatly among the single, almost transparent stones with the minimum of flaws, which can serve as gems in rings, necklaces, and earrings. If the gems are carved, or if they are items of great antiquity with a legitimate historical background, they then accelerate in value as collectors' pieces. The layman who undertakes this kind of jade study should consult an expert on antiques as well as a jeweler.

However, some very beautiful jades (nephrite and jadeite) are available for ring mountings, earrings, and necklaces. The Chinese have usually imported their jadeite from Northern Burma and more anciently from Turkestan. But the jades are found in such widely separated places as Central Asia, Guatemala, Siberia, California, Alaska, Wyoming, and Japan. The Aztecs and Mayas produced some fine carvings in jade, but no one is certain where their mines were located, or where they obtained the rough stones.

From the earliest days of their history, jade has been the most favored gem stone among the Chinese, and for a real knowledge of jade, you must study their works on it from about the year 2000 B.C. Collections of Chinese carvings in jade can be seen in many museums throughout the world. From 200 B.C. on, the Chinese were producers of the most exquisite work.

A green jade gem, in any mounting, should be checked to ascertain that it is not green turquoise, dyed agate, a fine piece of fluorite, serpentine, aventurine, malachite, or some other green stone which can pass for real jade to the uninitiated. Each of these "substitutes" has a beauty of its own, but if you want green jade (jadeite or nephrite) be sure you get it, and nothing else.

The possession of jade is said to give the owner power, knowledge, pure thoughts, and long life—and in some instances, immortality!

Kunzite

This gem is one that has been gaining favor with people who love a beautiful gem stone and appreciate a rare one. It is not well known or popular, consequently it is not as yet in great demand or expensive.

The mineral family it belongs to is called spodumene, and the kunzite has several relatives. One is green; another is yellowish to yellow-green. We will consider only the fabulous crystal-clear pink kunzite which ranges from very pale pink to deep lavender. Descriptions of the choicest stones vary, according to the person defining the gem. Some will say it is a clear rose pink, limpid blushing pink, light lilac pink, light wisteria pink, or

the pink of early dawn. Beauty is in the eye of the beholder. The vocabulary used to convey one's perception to another person is an individual sort of thing, but however the kunzite is described, it is one of the most beautiful of gems.

Seen from one direction the stone may appear almost devoid of color. From another, it shows a more definite hint of pink. Then viewed from still another direction the full, pure tint of the delicate pink is visible. The artisans who cut kunzite make certain, by keeping the shape deep, that the rich color and soft fire are seen to best advantage. A thinly cut stone would not fully reveal its qualities.

The mineral has been in the earth for millennia but was not "discovered," identified, or classified by name until this century. In 1902 a father-and-son team,

the Sicklers, found in California what was to them a strange new gem. In 1903 Dr. George F. Kunz, the famous gem expert for Tiffany's, identified and classified it as pink spodumene, and it was named "Kunzite" in his honor.

Being so newly "discovered," it has no legendary attributes, such as bringing good luck on alternate Tuesdays or being associated with astrological signs or planets.

One gem expert has said candidly that if he were given a year's time and a modest sum of money for expenses, he could make kunzite one of the most expensive gem stones in the world by presenting a fine kunzite ring, brooch, or pendant to each one of a number of famous people: a queen, a movie star, a great statesman, a king or president, one of the best-dressed women in the world, an opera singer, and a great sports star. He would then make certain that international news services got pictures and write-ups of these persons wearing the fabulous kunzites. The rush to buy would be on and when it became known that the amount of gem-quality kunzite in the world was limited, the price would start to rise. As it became known that the stone was found only in small areas in California, Madagascar, and Brazil, its rarity would be recognized further. Thus beauty, rarity and popular demand would send the price of kunzite up to "astronomical heights."

Kunzite ranks approximately with amethyst in hardness. This wonderfully clear, pink stone with its gentle fire is truly a gem to treasure.

Moonstone

Fine gem quality moonstone is actually scarce, although the mineral family from which it comes, feldspar, is one of the most plentiful in the world. Until fairly recent times the average person could generally recognize moonstone at first glance.

What we have always known as moonstone is the whitish, or gray-white, sometimes milky-white jewel stone, with a sort of blue sheen that seems to move across its face when it is turned this way and that. The moonstone with a consid

erable amount of this pearly-blue moving light is rare and valuable, and the more translucent the stone is the more it is preferred.

The closer the moonstone gets to an opaque plain white, the less value it has, not only because this kind occurs more commonly but also because it just isn't as attractive. Also, in the latter type, there is usually much less of that fascinating, luminous moving gleam. Some people describe this gleam as a soft and bluish moving opalescence, but that last word is apt to mislead you into relating the moonstone to the opal. They are not related.

In recent times several *new* colors of moonstone have been discovered in India. Some are green, and some are almost orange. The shimmery, moving gleam of light is a misty green or misty orange, as the case may be. Again, the more translucence and the more shimmer, the more valuable the gem is.

Come to think of it, there's no good reason we should be surprised to find moonstones in these shades. The moon itself appears in a number of colors. You've seen an orange harvest moon, and sometimes a moon that's greenish ("the moon is made of green cheese"). As for the blue-sheen moon, this is an actual scientific phenomenon. On rare occasion the moon does appear blue. But it happens so seldom that we use the old expression "once in a blue moon" to denote something that only happens now and then. Some folks think it never *does* happen, but it does.

Up until about 1925, the moonstone (the familiar one) had always been a very popular gem in the United States. Men wore them in stickpins for their ties, in cuff links, rings, and mounted as an ornament on a watch chain. Women wore them in rings, brooches, bracelets, earrings, and sometimes in necklaces. But fashions in jewel stones change from time to time, and the popularity of moonstones waned, for no apparent reason.

There is no reason either for moonstones not to regain their popularity. Real gem moonstone has become increasingly

difficult to find. Other than the new colors recently found (and these not in great quantity), moonstone has been growing scarcer by the year.

Moonstones range widely in cost from very little to a high point at which they are sold by the carat. As is the case with every gem family, the finest specimens are always of high value, because really superb examples of any gem are rare.

Moonstone is on the soft side, as gem stones go, but with the proper care, which should be given *all* jewelry, they will serve long and faithfully as beautiful adornments.

Moonstone is found in Ceylon, India, and Switzerland. Some good, small stones are not too difficult to locate, but larger ones of unflawed beauty are. Moonstone has always been considered lucky and is held in high esteem in the East. Orientals say there is a live spirit in it, for as the stone is turned this way and that the spirit can be seen moving.

There are many legends about moonstone. A person, for example, can be hypnotized by staring at a moonstone as it is turned slightly back and forth. There is of course some scientific basis for this: hypnotists have used the method of concentration on a moving shining light for several hundred years. Then, too, if your name is Mary or Matthew, this is *the* stone that definitely, by zodiac and tradition, is yours especially.

Moonstone is regarded as a splendid gift for lovers, as it arouses love. Also, if in the light of a full moon the stone is put into the mouth, it will foretell with certainty whether the owner's love life will be happy or unhappy. Monday is the day moonstone is at its peak for forecasting the future and for bringing the most luck. A dream about moonstones means danger is lurking ahead.

The Hindus thought moonstone was the congealed, solidified magic rays of the moon, and in India it was considered a sacred stone. Pope Leo X (around 1500) was supposed to have had a moonstone that grew dimmer and lost color as the moon waned, then gradually regained its shining glow as the moon grew fuller. Moonstone is said to cure epilepsy and nervousness, and to cause fruit trees to bear more abundantly.

Women were once punished for listening to secret conversations by having their ears pierced. This was also done to *prevent* overhearing such conversations. But as consolation for such agony the woman was given moonstone earrings to wear. So if a woman is willing to have her ears pierced, some man should be gallant enough to give her a fine set of moonstone earrings to ease the pain.

Opal

The opal is a gem so distinctive that everyone identifies its many-colored flashing lights on sight. Jewelers say that when it is artificially made the "fake" can be recognized as such by the least expert. An opal *can* be doctored with dyes, or made in a sliced doublet, but the result is only partly opal and easy to spot.

The most familiar opals have nearly opaque white or more translucent white backgrounds; however, some have a black or a reddish background. All of these vary greatly in the color of their fire; some show only red and orange lights, and some have green in addition and perhaps yellow and blue. The black opal may have these colors and purple as well. In short, opals show just about every shade of every color in a variety of combinations. Classifications of opal are given in some of the books listed in the bibliography.

Opals have not been found in many ancient archaeological diggings for a very good reason: they do not last for thousands of years. They contain from about

six to ten percent water, which dries out over the years, causing them to become quite brittle and to lose their hardness. The fire from this gorgeous jewel is made by the cracks in it; thus its beauty is also one of its weaknesses, not that the cracks are visible to the naked eye. If the cracks are visible without a magnifying lens, the gem is not considered a fine opal.

The superstition that opals bring bad luck is due to several factors. Actually, they have been considered very good luck throughout most of their written history, but in much earlier days, when jewelers did not understand how to handle and work the stones properly, they often broke as they were being cut, polished, or mounted. Naturally, that was bad luck.

In Sir Walter Scott's novel, *Anne of Geierstein*, Lady Hermione wore an enchanted opal in her hair. It gave off fiery red flashes when she was angry, but sparkled very prettily when she was happy. One time when a few drops of Holy Water were sprinkled on the gem, it lost its fire and sparkle. At the same time the lady became ill and was carried to her room and placed in bed. The next day all that was found of her and the gem was a heap of ashes in her bed.

Because of this story opals gained a wide reputation for bad luck. Empress Eugenie, wife of Napoleon III of France, refused to wear them, as did many others, some well-read and some not so well-read. On the other hand, Queen Victoria laughed at the superstition, and as her daughters married she gave them opals for wedding gifts. The daughters all fared well.

In medieval times all blond maidens wanted a necklace of opals, as this was considered an absolute guarantee to prevent their hair from fading or darkening. The opal was also thought to make a person invisible whenever he wished, and for that reason was called *Patronus furum* (patron of thieves). Shakespeare wrote of the gem in *Twelfth Night:* ". . . and the tailor make thy doublet of changeable taffeta, for thy mind is a very opal."

As always with fine jewel stones, given proper care, opals will last a long time. To see them is a constant delight, and as they range in price from moderate to high, it is possible to own one.

Pearl

The pearl is one gem that does not come from the earth. There is a line in an old hymn that reads: "Pearls from the ocean and gems from the mines," which is nice but not exactly correct, for the pearl *is* a gem that forms in mollusks (clams, oysters, and such) which can be found in *both* salt and fresh water.

Some small foreign body, a grain of sand for example, gets inside the bivalve creature and layers of pearly material form around it. In the true pearl (not the cultured) the layers build up somewhat like those of an onion, but in concentric circles. There is mineral content in this organic build up. Technical names and explanations are given in some of the books listed in the bibliography.

Another difference between pearls and other gems is in weight. Pearls are not measured by the carat. In museums they may be described as so many inches or millimeters in size, but their weight is given in *grains*. One grain of pearl is equal to one-quarter carat of gem stone weight, so it takes four grains of pearl to equal 1 carat in weight of other jewel stones.

There have always been many genuine pearls but always, as with other gems, large and perfect ones are rare. Real pearls are now becoming more and more scarce for several other reasons: one is the increasing contamination of the waters where the pearl-producers live, and the other is that many mollusk-producing areas have been partially exhausted by being overworked.

Genuine pearls come in a number of shades from white on through pink, blue, brown, gray, and black. Experts judge them by size, shape, color, luster, and degree of perfection (freedom from flaws). There are many pearl fanciers but very few experts, so it is usually wise to depend on a jeweler for advice when purchasing these gems.

According to all the writings that have come down to us, pearls have been ad-mired and treasured by peoples of many nations—Egypt, Arabia, China, India, and Persia among them. The Romans valued pearls so highly that at one time a law forbade anyone to wear them except persons of high rank. European explorers in the New World found many tribes of Indians in North and South America wearing pearl adornments. In 1579 King Philip II of Spain received a pearl from his representatives in Panama that weighed 1,250 grains. Julius Caesar was a great admirer of pearls and gave one as a gift that at the time was worth about $150,000: it would probably be worth ten times as much today.

There are large pearls in private collections throughout the world: the fabulous Peacock Throne of Iran has many

inset, including one of over 200 grains. But there are not as many pearls on constant, open exhibition in museums as there are other gems. Pearls will last a long time with proper care. Museum collections of pearls, however, require control of heat and light, among other details. They cannot be left in an ordinary showcase constantly exposed to sunlight, wide temperature variations, or acids and alkalis that might be present in the air. These conditions can dull a pearl's luster, the very quality which makes it so beautiful and so valuable. Therefore, an individual who owns pearls must also bear these things in mind and take precautionary measures.

For example, perspiration is very acid and harmful. Also, a pearl is relatively soft and can be marked by scratches, and it can be crushed by pressure. Most authorities seem to agree that natural pearls retain their qualities much longer than cultured pearls, especially in necklaces. Again, for the technical reasons, consult some of the books listed in the bibliography.

There have been many magic nostrums on the market which are supposed to preserve or restore to pearls their luster and color. Unfortunately they are about as effective as those purported to restore and grow hair. However, a good jeweler can clean, remount, or restring pearls so that they look like new, and without damaging them.

Earrings were once looked upon as a badge of slavery. Several Hebrew writings say that when Eve was banished from the Garden of Eden, part of her punishment included piercing her ears, but it is not clear whether this refers to the lobes or the drums. The Bible, in speaking of the New Jerusalem, says that the twelve gates of Heaven were of pearl. This perhaps explains the common phrase, the Pearly Gates of Heaven.

According to some legends, a dream of pearls means that you will be seeing faithful friends. In all ancient stories, the pearl is associated with faithfulness, friends, loyalty, modesty, and purity. It was one of the nine sacred gems usually listed in Sanskrit, Chinese, Arabic, and Burmese, and many Hindu idols had pearls inset as eyes.

Peridot

Peridot has the unique distinction of being the only gem crystal we know of at this time that sometimes comes to us as a gift from outer space. It occurs on earth in a limited number of locations. The mineral family is known variously as chrysolite, olivine and peridot, and it has been known to mankind far back in history. The peridots which have reached our earth from way out there among the stars have come to us embedded in meteorites. They are seldom of gem quality, but a few of these beautiful meteorite stones have been faceted and mounted in jewelry settings.

Choice peridot is transparent, and the color can be variously described as yellow-green, green with a golden tone, or simply a brilliant light green. Descriptive terms always depend upon the eyes and words of the beholder. Peridot has been called an Evening Emerald, for under artificial light the stone glows a brilliant green. Its name chrysolite, meaning "golden stone," is often used to designate gems from six or seven other mineral families.

As with all fine gem crystals, peridot seldom occurs in large sizes free of flaws. In nature, the larger gem crystals are, the easier they flaw, from such seismic disturbances as earthquakes and volcanic eruptions. Cutting and faceting are designed to eliminate the imperfections. So a twenty-carat stone in the rough may finally yield only three or four finished gems of one-half to three carats each. Also, as with many precious gems, peridots occur in small worn-down pebble-sized specimens weathered by tens of thousands of years of erosion in gem stone gravels.

Smaller peridots are fairly numerous, and not too expensive. These exquisite gems are often mounted in clusters of three or more, frequently in conjunction with other gems. Peridots of 2 or 3 carats are expensive, and a fine eight-carat stone is extremely rare. Any beyond this weight are collectors' or museum pieces. Peridot is a little softer than amethyst or emerald, and requires the care all fine gems should receive.

Early references to peridot called it by the name of "chrysolite," which meant the almost golden shade variety, and it was said to come from "The Serpent Isle." Later writers referred to the gem source as "an island in the Red Sea"; this is now known to be "St. John's Island" (Zerbirget). The mines there date far back in antiquity and once produced golden and gold-green peridots of large size and fine quality. As late as the nineteenth century the Khedive of Egypt had a monopoly on the mines, but since 1914 almost no mining has been done there.

Peridot has once again come into demand by discerning gem fanciers, but few of the choicer stones ever appear in our markets. Most remain east of Suez, prized by their owners and seldom traded or sold. The label "Ceylon peridot" or "Ceylon chrysolite" is suspect. These may be tourmalines, equally valuable and beautiful, but not peridot.

Once upon a time ecclesiastical treasures in European cathedrals included some fine, large peridots, but wars and pillage have dispersed many of them. The ones that "disappeared" probably exist today but cut down to smaller sizes and set in jewelry. Burma produces some good peridots although these tend toward a darker green. Brazil, Queensland, as well as Arizona and New Mexico also provide some fine, though usually small gem stones.

Two of the finest peridot displays containing some of the largest and best specimens are in the American Museum of Natural History in New York City and the Field Museum in Chicago.

Many legends state that chrysolite (as the more golden shade of peridot was called) possesses strong magic power. If the gem is set in gold, it has the power to dispel terrors of the night, fears, and bad dreams. However, according to Pliny, the Great Roman authority on such matters, for peridots to exert their strongest magic they must be pierced (made into beads) and strung on the hair of an ass. Then this piece of jewelry must be worn on the right arm.

Several experts, though not all, believe the second gem stone in Aaron's breast-plate was a chrysolite. And there is also an argument that has never been settled as to just which gem was used as the seventh foundation stone for the New Jerusalem of the Bible. Some authorities maintain that this too was chrysolite (or peridot). Another note about the power of the gem is contained in a statement made by the Bishop of Mainz about 1,100 years ago to the effect that ". . . in the chrysolite is shown true spiritual preaching accompanied by miracles."

Quartz is one of the most common minerals on earth. The names, forms, combinations, and colors are so numerous that entire books have been written just on quartz. Quartz may be of two kinds: the transparent crystal type, found in all colors, as well as a colorless variety, and the translucent to opaque type, which occurs in all colors and combinations of colors. Of the transparent types, amethyst is the most valuable. Also in this group is the absolutely clear rock quartz —the kind from which authentic fortune-tellers' crystal balls are made. Personally, I wouldn't believe a fortune-teller unless he (or she) had a true quartz crystal ball. If they start off by gazing into a phony ball—well, you can take it from there.

There is a beautiful transparent pink quartz, and one of fine yellow which should be called yellow quartz, but sometimes is called topaz— actually an entirely different family of stone of greater value, covered in another section. If the quartz is a pale yellow, or lemon-yellow, it may be called citrine, which is okay, but it is still quartz.

A brownish, smoky quartz is sometimes called smoky topaz. This is wrong, for there is a genuine smoky topaz which is of higher value. If brownish quartz is called *cairngorm*, this is legitimate, as it is the name given to it in Scotland, where this variety of quartz occurs. An even deeper blackish shade is called *morion*, which is legitimate too, but it is a dark quartz, not real topaz.

Then there is a fine transparent blue quartz which is quite rare, but if it is called *sapphire* quartz, the "sapphire" refers only to the blue color. This is *not* sapphire, just blue quartz. Real sapphire is far more costly.

Translucent members of the quartz family can include the tigereye and the hawk's-eye, already mentioned. There is also a milky quartz, sometimes passed off as moonstone. If there is no moving sheen of bluish light showing as the stone is turned, it is not moonstone but milky quartz. A rare and quite beautiful relative is the iris quartz, which from ancient times passed as imitation opal. Due to internal fracture, light is broken up and given off in dazzling rainbow colors, but this stone is still quartz, *not* opal.

From here on identification of specimens becomes more complex, as there are quartz family members ranging from the less translucent to opaque. There are many familiar names, for all quartz stones have been known, worked, carved, cut, used, and worn in various settings since very ancient times, and in almost every country. Here are a few of them:

Bloodstone is green with red streaks, spots, or splotches. According to the legends of various lands, it is good for stopping excessive bleeding. It can also bring

lightning, thunder, and rain. Spaniards found that Mexican Indians carved it in the shape of a heart, among other forms.

Carnelian is found in light to dark shades of red and red-brown. It is an ancient stone and has been popular in every land throughout history. It is said to bring good luck and bravery, also hope and comfort to a woman in pain. It especially protects the wearer from falling roofs or collapsing walls, and it is said to be good for driving away phantoms. Napoleon Bonaparte owned an engraved carnelian, which later was worn by Napoleon III on his watch chain.

Agate, aventurine, moss agate, and onyx are all beautiful quartz stones that have been and still are used for rings, bracelets, beads and every sort of adornment.

Sardonyx was used for the fine cameos that were cut during the Greek and Roman eras. There are many varieties from which to choose.

Jasper occurs, among other colors, in blue, yellow, and green. Green jasper is said to be a rainmaker if the proper incantation is recited. Yellow jasper has been all but immortalized by the fact that the famous carved head of Egyptian Queen Nefertiti was cut from it. Models, copies, and pictures of this masterpiece are found all over the world.

The Sumerians cut and engraved various quartz stones as cylinder seals and they used them later as ring seals. As the Sumerians invented writing, quartz is probably one of the first gem stone materials to be written on, and also to be used as a stamp to make a written impression (in clay). Some thousands of years ago the Egyptians made beads, scarab figures, and other jewelry from many of the quartz stones (including the transparent amethyst, prize of the family).

There are examples in various museums of carved quartz stones (again including the precious amethyst) that were popular in Greece and Rome. These sometimes show the upper half of the body of a man with a hand upraised, pronouncing judgment. Sometimes just the head and shoulders are shown, but again with the hand raised. These are said to have been especially good to have around during a lawsuit.

The quartz family provides dozens of varieties of jewel stones. This section can include only some of the better known, but museums and jewelers will show you many others.

Ruby

At first glance beautiful garnets or fine red spinels may be mistaken for rubies. Many royal crown jewels, thought for centuries to be rubies, have turned out to be spinels.

The ruby and the sapphire are the two precious "children" of the corundum "family." They are the same mineral, but of different colors. The sapphire occurs in all colors *except* red (though it does come in pink), and is sometimes colorless. The ruby occurs in several shades of red. But the really rare and most highly valued ruby is the kind (color) called "pigeon-blood," which actually resembles the blood of a pigeon, a rich red with just a hint of purple.

Like most precious gem stones, ruby that is nearly unflawed and of that precise, rare color seldom is found in large sizes. It is more apt to be found in weights of less than three carats. Rubies of five carats are uncommon, and few are known to be over thirty carats, although there is one that is nearly a hundred. Choice rubies average about a tenth the size of choice diamonds and occur far less frequently. It is no wonder then that, carat for carat, the splendid ruby is worth more than two or three times a diamond of equal quality.

Oddly, a star ruby is far more uncommon than a star sapphire, its family relative. And a *perfect* star ruby is extremely rare. Sometimes the stone is flawed or too cloudy, or the six points of the star are vague or unequal. The very 'inclusions" that make the star effect in the gem, when faulty, can also detract from the value. The inclusions in wrong positions caused cloudiness, and irregular and indistinct star lines.

Some gem experts can tell with reasonable accuracy where a ruby comes from just by looking at it. Most of the fine stones come from Burma, especially the pigeon-blood kind. Some beautiful rubies come from Thailand, but frequently are a little darker than the Burmese. The Island of Ceylon, once called Serendip, that fabulous producer of so many kinds of gems and site of many serendipitous discoveries, has long been famous for its rubies, but these tend to run to the lighter shades. The Chinese called Ceylon the "island of gems" and Marco Polo said no other place had rubies like Ceylon—but he was not an expert and was doubtless just dazzled.

Ruby is a hard stone, about the same as its brother sapphire. That "about" may be puzzling. Rubies vary slightly in hardness, being generally a bit softer than sapphire, although both are the same mineral.

This seeming lack of one hundred percent exactness in the hardness of specific gem stones is puzzling, for it is logical to expect jewels of the same mineral to be of equal hardness. It may be that the molecules are packed a little tighter in one amethyst than in another. This is an interesting but technical subject you may want to read up on. Nature never makes

each gem in a mineral family *exactly* the same.

As with emerald, a ruby by any *two* names is suspect. It is proper to speak of a ruby coming from Africa, Burma, South America, or from other places where it is found, but when the name is prefixed with such terms as "balas," "cape," "aldan," it means that the gem stone in question *resembles* a ruby but is not the real article.

Never make faces at a ruby in a museum, and *never* ignore it. Like many jewels, it is said to grow dull if slighted or not worn and seen. All old-time authorities agreed this was especially true of rubies.

The Hindus valued the ruby far more than other jewels and called it King of Precious Stones and Leader of Gems. They also divided the ruby into castes, according to whether it was first, second, third, or fourth rate in flawlessness and beauty. No inferior stone was allowed contact with a superior one because this would contaminate the better gem and diminish its magic powers, which were great.

The Kalpa tree, mentioned earlier, bore dazzling red rubies as its ripened fruit. In India, those who donated jewels to shrines rated high with their gods, and he who gave rubies to honor Krishna was almost assured of being reborn an emperor in a future reincarnation. This corresponds, more or less, with beliefs in old China, where a mandarin's rank was indicated by the color of the gem he was allowed to wear, and a red jewel stone, preferably ruby, meant he was a key figure among the great.

In Siam the "in" people wore red silks and rubies on Sunday. But men of other countries stated that Friday was the only proper day to wear the clear ruby, while Wednesday absolutely called for the star ruby. Even Ivan the Terrible of Russia stated that ruby was very good for the heart, brain, and memory, and that it purified the blood.

Jewelers of France in the 1880's called the ruby the Gem of Gems, the Dearly Loved Stone, and other adulatory names.

A thirteenth-century prescription to cure liver ailments required powdered ruby. The mixing of this wonder cure was a secret, however. A ruby also made a very fine doctor's fee.

Quite commonly the ruby was associated with the sun, and it was often thought to be a strong preserver of mental and physical health. Some went so far as to say that it was a powerful aid in controlling amorous desire. Legends the world over agreed that the ruby was a splendid settler of disputes and had a sure power for reconciliation.

Sapphire

As we have seen, sapphire and ruby are the two costly gem members of the corundum mineral family, and are almost identical in all scientific aspects *except* for their coloration. The technicalities of these color differences are covered in some of the books listed in the bibliography; the details are fascinating but not essential here.

When most people speak of a sapphire, they have in mind a jewel of rich blue; and the most prized and rarest sapphire, therefore the most expensive one, is just that. Gem experts call it *Kashmir* because the choicest sapphires have come from there. Even if a sapphire of that very select color comes from another place, it may still be described as Kashmir blue.

Others use terms such as royal blue, or cornflower blue. Somehow the latter does not bring the true sapphire blue to mind, but as has been said, individuals describe gems in varying ways. A poet has described sapphire as the blue of a clear sky just minutes after sundown.

Sapphire occurs also in a clear, colorless specimen, as well as in yellow, orange, pink, green, and violet, and in a shade so dark it could almost be called blue-black. The stone is transparent if it is "choice," but that very dark shade is almost opaque. Because there is much more sapphire in the world than ruby, it is not as expensive as its red relative, but the price of a perfect Kashmir blue sapphire about equals that of a diamond. Sapphires in the other colors are not in as great public demand, as few people know of them, and thus they are not so costly, but they are all of extraordinary beauty.

Again, as with other gems, names can be misleading. The "Madagascar Emerald" may be a green sapphire. The "Chinese Amethyst" may be a violet sapphire. The correct labels should be "green" or "violet" sapphire—just the color designation and the word *sapphire*. Naturally, it is not only legitimate but informative if the name of the country from which the stone came is added. If just the word *sapphire* is used, look for the familiar blue, and of course expect to see stones of varying shades of blue.

For example, if the tag reads "sapphire —Montana, U.S.A.," these jewels are genuine and of good quality with few flaws, but the color is often more of a steely blue, not the rarer, softer shade. Sapphires also come from Ceylon, Burma, Thailand, and Australia.

It is not true that the best stones come only from Kashmir; some fine ones come from other sources. But in general, Burma ranks next to Kashmir in producing fine blue sapphires, though some are on the dark side. Ceylonese and Thai stones are

apt to be too pale a blue, while the Australian stones may be a little too dark, not always rated "choice" in all respects.

Actually, the blue color should be deep enough to show richly by day, and yet remain a fine glowing blue in artificial light. This is true of the Kashmir color. Some sapphires that look well enough by day appear dead blue or blue-black as soon as the sun goes down. If the perfect ones are not available, the slightly paler blue sapphire holds color and fire better in less light.

Star sapphires occur far more often than star rubies, but a fine one is rare. They often show as too cloudy, or the rays are either not distinct or unevenly marked. One of the largest, over 540 carats, is the "Star of India" in the American Museum of Natural History in New York. This jewel was involved in the big robbery there in the 1960's. The three crossbars that give the star effect are supposed to represent Faith, Hope and Destiny.

Soothsayers and fortune-tellers have stated that sapphire enabled them to read, know, and interpret the most baffling and obscure oracles, signs, and portents. And they get solid backing, for witches, too, have claimed that the stone works wonders for them.

Sapphire was also reported an excellent all-purpose medicine if well ground up; when the cost was prohibitive, several other less costly blue gems could be substituted. Ivan the Terrible of Russia claimed that sapphire strengthened the heart and muscles and endowed a person with courage. Others of his era claimed even more for the gem. They said it was an antidote for poison—it killed snakes on sight—and if engraved with the figure of a ram or a man, the sapphire cured all ills and could elevate the owner to a very high position.

The Kalpa gem tree of the Hindus, mentioned earlier, had roots of sapphire, and the stone was usually included in the lore of many lands as one of the nine sacred jewels. In parts of the Orient, Saturday was the day to dress in blue and of course wear blue sapphire. Certain gems were assigned to certain hours of the day and night when each stone's potency for good luck was supposed to be strongest; sapphire is best from ten to eleven in the morning. The color blue and the blue stone indicate wisdom, and lofty, generous thinking. In addition, the gem is associated with the study of the heavens and the stars.

Sapphire has many sacred associations through old legends and traditions. Some writers of olden times claimed that the Ten Commandments were written on sapphire. Around the eleventh and twelfth centuries the sapphire was much esteemed as the appropriate stone for ecclesiastical rings; its power for good was revered because it was the color of the pure blue of the heavens.

There is a cross inset with pearls and nine superb blue sapphires in the Cluny Museum in Paris. It was a pendant to the crown of a Gothic King of Spain who ruled in the seventh century. Sapphire is by tradition a regal gem. As such, historically it was often set in the bracelets, necklaces, pendants, crowns, and jewelry of royalty.

In the imperial crown of Great Britain, there are two large and historic blue sapphires. One was once set in the coronation ring of Edward the Confessor, and the other is called the Stuart gem, and later came into the possession of King George III. In the British Sword of State is a fine, rare yellow sapphire. Napoleon Bonaparte was presented with two large sapphires which were once owned by Charlemagne. So the association of the gem with royalty, bravery, and conquerors seems to hold true.

It seems only natural that the sapphire should be considered a healing stone and a sacred and royal symbol because in all its colors and particularly in the heavenly Kashmir blue it is one of nature's most lovely stones.

Spinel

The sparkling spinel is a hard stone. It comes colorless, or in red, rose, yellow, green, blue or violet, and is often found in the very same places as sapphire and ruby. In fact, the red and blue members of this splendid mineral family are famous, because for centuries uncounted they have been mistaken, and quite logically too, for ruby and sapphire—the best, and most embarrassing, example of this confusion being two "rubies," now known to be spinel, among the British crown jewels.

The most ancient and historic of those royal gems is sometimes called the "Timur Ruby," and sometimes "Tribute of the World." In 1398 Tamerlane (Timur the Lame) swept through India. In Delhi he seized a cart load of jewels, among them a big red "ruby" of more than 350 carats.

Centuries passed, and rulers and kings did also. Kingdoms changed back and forth through wars, and so did their fortunes in gems. At one point in its journeys, this great "ruby" came into the possession of Emperor Shah Jahan of India, the same who built the Taj Mahal. Jahan also owned the fabulous Peacock Throne, with its twelve pillars, each decorated with two peacocks. These twenty-

four birds glittered with pearls, rubies, diamonds, sapphires, and every sort of gem, *including* the enormous Timur "ruby."

In 1851 Queen Victoria received a present from the East India Company—the very same Timur "ruby." It was mounted in a necklace, along with other gems, and became a part of the crown jewels. Engraved on the back of the big "ruby," in small Arabic letters, were the names of people who had owned the gem even before Tamerlane had grabbed it!

Years later the "Timur" or "Tribute of the World" was identified, not as a ruby, but as one of the largest and finest red spinels ever known. It is a very beautiful stone, but today the value of a real ruby of such size would be so great that it would take a computer to figure the difference.

The "Black Prince's Ruby" was sent by Pedro the Cruel, King of Castile, to Edward the Black Prince, a son of Edward III of England and commander of the English forces in Europe, who had placed Pedro on his throne in 1367. The "ruby" was eventually inherited by Henry V, who wore it in his helmet when he defeated the French at the Battle of Agincourt in 1415, although his army was outnumbered three to one. All rubies are thought to protect the wearer from injury, and after Agincourt the "Black Prince's Ruby" was considered particularly good luck. It was later mounted in the British royal crown, where it remains today. But again, Pedro the Cruel's gift has been found to be a tremendous spinel, about two inches long, irregular in shape and very beautiful. And again the loss to the Crown in finding the great ruby to be relatively common spinel is shocking.

Because spinels resembled other jewels and were often mistaken for them, this family of gems has few legendary attributes and little association with magic or marvelous powers. The Hindus realized that all red stones were not fine ruby, so although they still called some spinels a kind of ruby, they put them in lower castes, and, as with other low-caste gems, they were never allowed to be mixed with high-caste jewels.

Fine spinels are found in Ceylon, Burma, Thailand, and, in the United States, in New Jersey and New York. It would be more satisfactory if each spinel were called by its color—red, yellow, green, or whatever—but it is not too difficult to recognize the "tags." For example, red spinel may be called "spinel ruby" or "balas ruby." The yellow and orange-yellow spinels may be labeled "rubicelles," while the green may be called "chloro-spinel" (as in chlorophyll).

Fine gem spinel is transparent, fairly hard, and has luster and light. The name derives from a Greek word meaning "a spark." For some reason it is not a widely popular stone, so with only moderate demand, the cost of it is not high.

Tanzanite

Tiffany's in New York, probably the most famous name in the world of gems and jewelry, has bestowed the title of tanzanite on some fabulously beautiful gem crystals discovered in 1967 in northern Tanzania. Some experts state that this discovery is one of the most exciting in the field of gem stones in nearly a century. The lovely blue of the tanzanite is something which must be seen to be appreciated.

But the mineral family of which tanzanite is a member has been known for nearly two centuries. It was named zoisite in 1805, some time after the Baron Sigismund Zois von Edelstein had identified the mineral. Nor is zoisite itself so uncommon: it is found in a number of European countries, as well as in Pennsylvania, North Carolina, and Tennessee.

Most mineral zoisite occurs as a dull gray or brown color when found in fair crystal form, and has little gem value. Another relative of tanzanite, thulite (same zoisite family), is found in Norway and occurs in. rose pink. This stone is occasionally of gem value. Oddly enough, some gem zoisite crystals are also found in Ducktown, Tennessee.

Yet none of these even remotely equals the tanzanites found in a small area in the foothills of Mount Kilimanjaro in Africa. The gems from that locale, predominantly blue, are unique in clarity, color and size. If one of these tanzanites is turned in one direction it will show a brilliant blue color more beautiful than

sapphire; turned in another direction the color will show a purple almost as lovely as fine amethyst; turned a third way, the color will show a salmon-pink brown which may be described as flesh-colored. The tanzanite is, in short, "trichroic" (three-colored).

It is desirable to bring out the fabulous blue in cutting or faceting the tanzanite, as this is the rarest and most striking color of the gem, and lends itself to settings with other stones. Tiffany's has one of the largest and most beautiful displays of the gem.

The tanzanite's fire or "dispersion" factor, especially that of the splendid blue color, is comparatively high; for this reason the tanzanite alone of all the zoisite family can be classed with any other splendid gem. But as in all gem stone families, large, clear, nearly flawless tanzanites are rare. The rule always remains: the larger any gem stone is the greater is the chance of flaws occurring. Also, as with all stones, the color is an important factor. A tanzanite of the perfect blue brilliant hue in five, ten, or twenty carats is of greater value than a paler, or darker, or duller one of twice the size and weight.

Because the tanzanite is so newly found, it has no legends or superstitions connected with it. Like many of the most beautiful gem stones, it is nowhere nearly as hard as sapphire or diamond. But given the proper care, as indicated for other gems, the tanzanite can prove to be one of your most cherished and admired gems. The cost per carat is still fairly moderate but it is a rare gem and likely to gain in value as a collector's item.

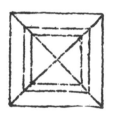

Topaz

The very word topaz conjures up in the mind a beautiful gem. It is a jewel stone that has been honored in the literatures of the world for thousands of years. Most people think of it is a transparent golden yellow. However, as with many other mineral stones, topaz occurs in other tints. For example, there is a crystal-clear topaz, one a sort of orange-yellow, and another a honey-brown (dark sherry). One is light green, one a pale blue, and finally there is a pink variety. The natural pink topaz is rare, but the stone can be "pinked" artificially. A jeweler can distinguish between the natural stone and the pinked stone.

There is no confusion about the names; the specific color, plus "topaz," is a true description, but experts have said that some of the blue topaz may be tagged as "aquamarine," which is unfortunate, because a fine aquamarine of the right color is worth more than a topaz.

Gem topaz is found in many places, often in large sizes, in Utah, California, Colorado, Brazil, Mexico, Japan, Russia and other countries too.

The best specimen of a large-sized topaz is in the American Museum of Natural History in New York. This jewel weighs six hundred pounds and is colorless. The same museum also contains a

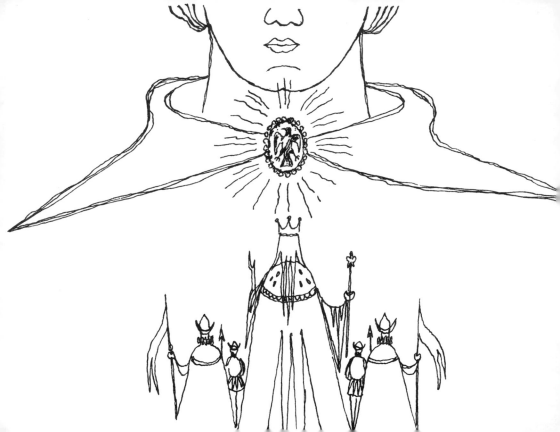

beautiful blue topaz from Japan cut with 444 facets.

Jewelers who handle the topaz speak of its distinctive slippery "feel"—a feel quite unlike that of most other stones. They say it has a particular, shiny glisten, as well, and being a fairly hard gem, holds its polish well. Also, when rubbed, it develops some static electricity.

Some topaz shares with several stones a tendency to fade, to lose or change color after long and constant exposure to strong light. Specimens of the tawny (yellow-brown) color have been known to turn entirely clear after being on display in museums over a period of years. Some blue topaz also tends to pale under the same conditions. For this reason, topaz is kept under cover except at exhibition times.

The topaz, like the ruby, figures in a famous true story involving gem mistaken identity. Set in the royal crown of Portugal was a tremendous jewel of 1,680 carats. For years this was known as the Braganza "diamond," so called for the long Braganza royal line. But it was finally correctly classified as a topaz and not a diamond. The difference in money value between such a topaz and a similar diamond could be a million dollars; more or less; no one could be absolutely certain.

The Greeks had a word for topaz, which they got from Sanskrit, in which language it meant "to shine," and also implied "fire."

Topaz is mentioned as being one of the jewels in Aaron's breastplate, and as the ninth foundation stone of Biblical New Jerusalem. The middle of the trunk of the Kalpa jewel tree of the Hindus was topaz. It has been said that a topaz engraved with the figure a falcon will put the owner in the good graces of emperors, royalty—anyone in high authority, and will bring enormous assistance from them.

Some ancient astrologers associated topaz with the planet Jupiter, but others argued it was influenced by the moon or the sun. It was among the nine sacred gems mentioned in Burmese, Chinese, Arabic, and Sanskrit writings. One tradition said the topaz exerted its strongest power for good luck if worn on Sunday, but another tradition said Tuesday. The best hour of the day to wear it was set between four and five P.M.

It is said that a dream of topaz before a journey means that absolutely no harm will come to you enroute or even after you arrive at your destination. Also, there is a topaz prescription for eyes that tire easily. Soak a topaz in wine for three days; then remove. Use the solution to moisten the eyeballs. The curative powers will last five days.

Tourmaline

Tourmalines should be among the most admired and popular of gems for they come in a variety of wonderful colors and they show beautiful "fire." But the mineral is found widely throughout the world and mankind seldom values highly the more common beauties of nature.

Tourmalines vary in hardness: Some rank slightly below some of the quartz gems and others are about equal to emeralds. However, lack of hardness is no problem. Like amethyst and emerald, tourmaline will last for thousands of years. The Chinese have engraved and carved figures with it for many centuries, and ancient examples survive and are displayed in museums.

Tourmaline has often been confused with other gems. Like spinel, topaz, and quartz, its wide range of colors has caused it to be mistaken for emeralds, topaz, and sapphires.

There is even a mix-up in the name "tourmaline," from the East Indian "tormali" that at one time designated the reddish carnelian. Zircons, discussed in a

later section, occur in various colors, and tourmalines were often wrongly identified with them as well. So tourmaline gems, called by many names (including "schorl"), have no individual ancient legendary background in the literature of jewel stones.

Jewel quality stones of tourmaline come from such far apart places as Burma, Elba, Russia, Madagascar, South America, and in the United States, from California, Maine and Connecticut. One place in California, Pala Chief Mine, yields kunzites already mentioned, as well as fine tourmalines.

Modern usage of various names for different colored tourmalines confuses gem fanciers. Red or red-pink tourmalines are tagged "rubellites"; violet ones, "siberites"; and yellow-green ones, "ceylonese peridots." These names should be translated back into the color plus "tourmaline" for proper identification, for instance, "violet tourmaline."

Tourmalines are fascinating stones. One color may show from one direction and another color from another direction. Sometimes a single stone may show two separate bands of color, and some even three. Under friction tourmaline will develop a static electrical charge and attract or repel certain materials.

It is a very complicated mineral and experts agree on only some facts, not others. Research on this gem stone is needed to discover, among other things, what gives it its various properties of color.

Turquoise

Since the days of the ancient Egyptians, the ubiquitous turquoise has been known throughout the world and has always been in great demand. Fortunately it is found in quantity in many countries and the price of a good turquoise is not beyond the average person. Some authorities state that the name of this popular stone is of Tartar origin; others state that it got its name because it was first discovered in Turkistan; and still others say the name comes from Turkey because in the Middle Ages much turquoise came to Europe through that country and was called "turkish" stone.

Actually, the finest stones have usually come from Persia, from the mines near Nishapur, one of the oldest of cities. But the turquoise of the Egyptians, about 2000 b.c., and the gem stones mentioned in the Bible, probably came from the mines in the Sinai peninsula. The turquoise from Egypt is generally greenish, although some turquoises of the more valuable true blue color are found there. In the eastern lands of Persia, Turkey, Egypt, Arabia, and India, the turquoise is considered a stone of good luck and good fortune.

Turquoise is found in many places far

from Asia Minor and the Middle East: Mexico, the Orient, Australia, and many parts of the western United States, including Colorado, Texas, Arizona, New Mexico, Nevada, and California.

Historically, Montezuma and the natives of Mexico, Central America, and South America, prized turquoise highly, but there is confusion here, for their turquoise was often green jade or perhaps poor-quality emerald. Any green stone was thought to be precious, and the Spanish conquistadores seized all, believing them emeralds. Some of these have only lately been classified precisely as fine emerald, but others as aquamarine, jade, or turquoise.

Only one quality of turquoise is rare and valuable. This is the "robin's egg blue," or as some describe it, "sky blue"; and the costliest must be free of cracks, flaws, and discoloration by other chemical and mineral inclusions.

Turquoise is porous and is affected by liquids (even perspiration from the wearer) or exposure to the' sun and the elements, and it contains some water (as do opals), so the beautiful blue may turn green after long use or exposure and thus lose value.

Turquoise is not hard, ranking below quartz stones (amethyst for example) in the "pecking" order (explained in another section); but as always with gem stones, given proper care its beauty will last a long time, perhaps as long as the stones from ancient Egyptian crypts.

The legends about turquoise and the

magical qualities attributed to it are numerous. About 1250 A.D., it was believed in Europe that wearing a turquoise protected the wearer from falling—from a horse, a building, or a mountain. In Persia it was said that if a horse wore a bridle set with turquoise, the animal would not stumble or throw the rider. By 1600, almost no man of quality thought his hand well-adorned unless he wore a turquoise ring, but strangely enough women seldom wore turquoise.

The Persians considered turquoise their national stone, a protection from all harm, and ranked it as a sign of the Koran and their religion, engraving Koranic quotations in it. American Indians —Navajos and Apaches—considered turquoise indispensable to a medicine man, and a turquoise attached to an arrow assured a warrior that he would never miss his target. In England, as late as 1890, a lady stated that the hue of turquoise indicated the health of the wearer: if it faded, the wearer was ill; when the stone resumed its original color, the patient had recovered.

The legendary properties of this beautiful gem may be discounted by many wearers today, but it is as widely popular as ever and available set in fashionable jewelry from many periods and parts of the world.

Zircon

The wonderful zircon is an ancient gem, mentioned frequently throughout history, but although it is found in many places in the world, *fine* zircons are not common. The zircon occurs in Australia, Ceylon, Thailand, India, Russia, Canada, the United States, and elsewhere, and has always been popular in the Orient.

The zircon family of jewels has a wide range of color: yellow, orange, red, blue, green, brown, violet, and some are colorless. Choice white (colorless) zircons, when cut and faceted expertly, closely resemble diamonds and show considerable fire, especially under artificial light.

Choice zircons in the other shades of color also show lovely fire when finely faceted.

In older accounts, zircons were often called by a number of names, for it was not known that these were all one family. *Hyacinth, Jacinth, Zargun,* and *Zarqun* were actually zircons of different colors. Also, as in the confusion between other gems, in old stories and accounts occasionally when "diamond" was mentioned "zircon" was meant.

Zircon is softer than diamond, but stands up under wear when treated with the care all good gems deserve. It varies

in hardness among the members of its own family, from a little below amethyst, for example, to a bit over it. Also, zircon happens to be one of the "heaviest" stones—the molecules are packed firmly —and four carats or zircon might appear the size of only a three-carat gem of a less dense jewel stone.

Several authorities state that the breastplate of Aaron probably contained a yellow zircon as one of its twelve gems. Also, the eleventh foundation stone of New Jerusalem was supposedly zircon. In Greece and Rome engraving figures in jewel stones developed into an art. The zircon was a favorite, and the craftsmen cut intaglios in it; the design was concave, or hollowed out, the opposite of a cameo, which is a raised design. Zircon is mentioned as a mystery stone in the *Arabian Nights*, only there it is called *jacinth*. The foliage of the Hindu Kalpa tree was of zircon, except for the very young leaves.

Blue zircon was said to provide you with heavenly wisdom, and any zircon would elevate your thoughts to such a degree that you became humble and just and naturally treated the weak and poor with kindness and generosity.

In various countries the yellow zircon was associated with the zodiac sign of Leo, thus with lions and courage. A bright red zircon was said to be the cure for all insomnia. But colors and what they stood for differed from country to country. Even within each nation the symbolism of colors changed with the passage of centuries. During the Middle Ages the yellow zircon was a proper stone for both the sun and for Sunday. Later, the white (colorless) member of the family also had these associations.

From ancient times on up through the Middle Ages a zircon was considered a must for travelers, as it was a powerful protection against wounds and plagues. Most important, it would warn its owner of plague by turning dull if an infected person were near. This was not the limit of zircon magic: when powdered and mixed with laudanum, it was a cure for fevers caused by contaminated water or air. This might come in handy nowadays, with our fouled-up water and air.

If you are nervous when there's an eclipse of the sun or moon a zircon is said to calm the nerves, and in Sanskrit writings the stone was dedicated to the dragon who causes eclipses. By stroking a zircon and saying a few kind words, the dragon in gratitude would huff and puff the eclipse away. Another important attribute of the zircon is protection against lightning.

There has always been an argument as to which planet lends its influence to zircon: some say Mars and some say Jupiter, but there is agreement on how to wear the gem to relieve or prevent disease. Either wear it on the neck or mounted in a ring for the little finger of the *left* hand.

Aids in the Selection of Gems

SYNTHETIC AND IMITATION STONES

Nature never has supplied enough beautiful, natural gems for everyone. And life never has provided everyone with enough money to purchase the gems he admires. But the desire for personal adornment is inherent, and the demand for ornamental, less expensive jewelry has been met throughout the history of mankind by clever artisans.

Glassmaking came into being about 3000 B.C., probably in Sumeria or Egypt, and with it came the first man-made imitations of natural gems. Men learned how to add colors to glass so that reasonably attractive jewelry could be fashioned.

Later, the Greeks and Romans improved the craft, and many an ancient glass "ruby," "emerald," or "sapphire" was passed off as genuine.

Glass imitations continued to be made through the Dark Ages and the Middle Ages, and they are still being made today. They are commonly called "pastes," and at first glance, as the art of making them has improved, they look real. At present, plastics are also used to imitate gem stones, and plastic and glass imitations are widely used in costume jewelry.

Some synthetic gem stones are now quite plentiful and have approximately the same qualities of color, crystal form, and chemical formula as the "natural" stones. Only an expert can distinguish synthetic ruby, sapphire, and spinel from nature's products. Synthetic star sapphires and star rubies are also available at prices far below an "original." But so far, no true synthetic alexandrite, zircon, or aquamarine has been produced.

Only very, very small diamonds of gem quality have been made, and the cost of making them is prohibitive. However, since 1957 synthetic nongem-quality diamonds for industrial use have been made in the United States, although the cost is greater than that of the natural stone. This assures our country that we can be independent of foreign importation in time of war.

Emeralds are created through highly secret methods by several world-renowned companies, and these man-made stones are by no means inexpensive although they cost less than natural stones. Only an expert can distinguish between them.

Cultured pearls might be included under the "synthetic" label if it is interpreted to mean "fashioned" or made by man. The Japanese have developed the art of "growing" pearls by impregnating a mollusk with a foreign particle around which the nacre forms in somewhat the same way as "natural" pearls are formed.

In a "real" pearl, the layers of nacre form in concentric, circular layers, but in cultured pearls the layers form in regular circles. Sometimes a jeweler has to resort to x-ray to determine (by the shape of the layers) which is cultured and which is real.

Another kind of gem "imitation" utilizes only a part of a real stone (say sapphire) on top; the bottom part is glass or a slice of valuable stone. The two sections are glued together and called a "doublet." These can be very beautiful and cost far less than a solid gem.

With all this in mind, the fact remains that you should consult a jeweler before purchasing jewelry.

THEIR SETTINGS

People who admire gems eventually want to buy and wear them. In the process, they learn more about gems and jewelry, and this increases their enjoyment. But before purchasing a gem a jeweler should be consulted. Not even a broad knowledge of gems, acquired from reading such books as are listed in the bibliography, qualifies an individual to put to use his theories, nor would he have the proper equipment. He might learn to speak intelligently of a single or double refraction, but he would not own a refractometer to measure this. He might learn to relate the specific gravity ratings of gems, but he would not have the devices to determine specific gravity. Nor would he have an x-ray machine to show the difference between a natural and a cultured pearl. He perhaps could discuss the crystal forms of various gem stones, their chemical formulas, and pleochroism, but only the expert jeweler and his equipment could provide factual proofs.

For settings and mountings, the jeweler's judgment again should be relied upon. A customer may prefer a certain style of ring setting and, although the jeweler may admire his artistic taste in design, he may point out that such a setting does not allow the right amount of light to reach the stone to show it to the best advantage. Or he may suggest another design which provides maximum protection for a jewel that might otherwise be easily scratched or nicked.

A customer may ask for yellow gold for the mounting, but the jeweler may show him that the particular color of the gem is altered or weakened by the yellow, and suggest white gold. Sometimes platinum shows off the particular tint of a gem to better advantage. There are other alternatives too. The main body of the mounting can be of yellow gold and the prongs or cup of white gold. Or the reverse may be better. Where two or three different gems are to be mounted together, a lot more advice is needed.

The purer the gold the greater is its value, but a high gold content in a ring or any jewelry mounting is not desirable if the item is to be worn frequently. *Solid gold is twenty-four karats* (spelled with a "k," the measure of gold content and no relation to "carats," spelled with a "c," the measure of weight for gems). Eighteen karats is seventy-five percent gold, fairly soft and "wear-downable"; fourteen karats is harder and wears much longer.

THEIR CARE

Jewelry should not be tossed in a heap, as one gem stone may scratch another or the metal mountings. Each article of jewelry should have its own soft cushion

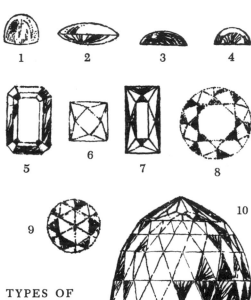

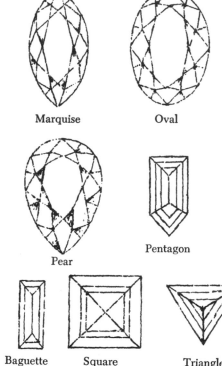

TYPES OF CUTTING

1-4—Cabochon styles
1. High cabochon
2. Lentil
3. Single
4. Hollow (cross sect.)
5. Emerald or step cut
6. French cut
7. Scissor cut
8. Circular brilliant
9. Old rose cut
10. Great Mogul diamond, in multiple rose cut

Marquise

Oval

Pear

Pentagon

Baguette

Square

Triangle

bed or velvet niche. Mistreated jewels lose their luster and brilliance.

Spray perfumes, colognes, deodorants, or hair-fixatives should not be applied near jewelry, and the jewel case should be kept closed. Some stones and pearls can be spotted by the alcohols, acids, and chemicals in spray preparations. Even the gems that are not permanently affected will become coated with gummy residue from the droplets of spray.

Dust and oily grime in the air will also eventually dull the appearance of jewelry. A jeweler, and only he, can recommend proper cleaning methods. It is also wise to take jewelry to a jeweler for a check-up and expert cleaning every year; the same applies to watches if really properly cared for. A jeweler can polish out nicks in gems if there are any. Above all, he can make certain that the stones are secure in their settings.

There are several other reasons for visiting a jeweler: to inspect new stones he has just acquired, or to alert him in advance to be on the look out for a certain kind of gem or piece of jewelry that you wish to purchase.

When about to purchase a piece, it is advisable to give the jeweler time to obtain several items from which to choose. If he knows what kind and size of gem you want, and the price range, he can search for choice examples. When estates are "sold off," fine jewelry is auctioned. Some of the stones may be especially fine but poorly cut. A jeweler can buy them at a reasonable cost and have the gems recut and reset for you.

Advance notice also gives a jeweler

time, for example, to wait until an associate returns from buying in Burma, Ceylon, South America, or Africa. Or he himself may be planning to visit auctions or gem markets abroad. The more time he has to examine available stones, the better specimens he can get. This holds true whether you want a modest set of rose quartz stones for earrings, a choice ring sapphire, or a multicarat diamond. And this is especially true if a certain weight, cut, and cost are specified and if two or more gems are to be matched. Matching stones *really* requires time.

PECKING ORDER AMONG GEM STONES

In 1823 the German mineralogist Friedrich Mohs set up a table of the relative hardness for minerals that is still used as a convenient "rule-of-thumb" reference in defining the pecking order of gems. It runs from ten (diamond) to one (talc). It is by no means precise for particular gem stones will vary up or down on the scale from an eighth to a half, depending on the origin of the stone and other conditions. With a modern gadget called a sclerometer, the hardness of minerals can be measured exactly. The following adaptation of the Mohs scale, based on the latest research, gives some idea of the average hardness of the gem stones discussed in this book and is easy for the layman to understand.

There are other qualities to be considered in judging gem stones, such as toughness, brittleness and lines of cleavage. For example, the jades (jadeite and nephrite) are moderately low on the Mohs scale, but their molecular structure renders them tough and durable. Diamond is harder, yet it can be shattered into two or more parts if struck on a cleavage line. Some gems shatter easily, while others do not.

If you watch a thief on television grabbing a handful of diamonds, emeralds and pearls and stuffing them all in his pocket, you will know he is an amateur. An expert would keep them separate and never allow the diamonds to scratch the emeralds and pearls. They would lose value.

HARDNESS	GEM STONE
10	Diamond
9	Ruby, Sapphire
8½	Alexandrite, Cat's-eye and Yellow Chrysoberyl
8	Topaz, Spinel
7½	Aquamarine, Emerald and other Beryl stones, Almandine Garnet, Zircon
7¼	Kunzite and other Spodumene stones, Pyrope Garnet
7	Jadeite, Quartz stones (some Amethyst is 7¼), Tourmaline
6½	Demantoid Garnet, Nephrite (the other Jade), Peridot, Tanzanite and other Zoisite stones
6	Moonstone, Opal, Turquoise
5	Lapiz Lazuli
4	Pearl

FOR FURTHER READING...

Those who wish to explore the fascinating world of gems further can start with these popular texts: *Wonders of Gems*, by R. M. Pearl (Dodd, Mead: New York, 1963); *The Story of Gems*, by F. H. Pough (Harvey House: New York, 1967); and *The Story of the Gems*, by H. P. Whitlock (Putnam: New York, 1947). By the time you finish these you'll be a fluent conversationalist on gem stones, and have a fair knowledge of the field. Now dip into *The Curious Lore of Precious Stones*, by G. F. Kunz (Lippincott: Philadelphia, 1913), a collection of legends and superstitions, true and imagined stories about jewels. It's a joy to read. The book is out of print, but your library should have a copy.

For further study, read *The World of Jewel Stones*, by M. Weinstein (Sheridan House: New York, 1958). This is a professional, detailed work, written so lucidly that you can get the *substance* from it even if you are weak in technical knowledge.

The books listed above contain information that is not given in *Enjoying Gems*, for I have avoided using technical terms, crystal forms, chemical formulas of gem material, as well as descriptions of technical procedures in cutting, faceting, and other related subjects.

For the confirmed jewel fan, the following books will provide even more information and interesting reading, but some of them require at least a basic knowledge of physics, math and chemistry. The works of Dana are practically a course in mineralogy and geology. Each of the titles suggested below gives further reading references:

Aaron's Breastplate by A. Paul Davis (Hoffman Press: St. Louis, 1960).

Chemical Chrystallography by C. W. Bunn (Oxford University Press: London, 1961).

Dana's Manual of Mineralogy, 16th edition, ed. by C. S. Hurlbut, Jr. (Wiley: New York, 1952).

Dana's System of Mineralogy, 7th edition, 3 vols., ed. by D. Plache, H. Berman and. C. Frondel (Wiley: New York, 1951).

Encyclopedia Americana—Gems; also see each gem stone by name.

Encyclopaedia Britannica—Gems; also see each gem stone by name.

Gems and Gem Materials, 5th edition, by E. H. Kraus and D. B. Slawson (McGraw-Hill: New York, 1947).

Gems and Precious Stones of North America by G. F. Kunz (Dover: New York, 1968).

Golden Bough, The, by J. G. Fraser (Macmillan: New York, 1951).

Handbook of Gem Identification, 5th edition, by Richard T. Liddicoat (Gemological: Los Angeles, 1957).

Investigation and Studies of Jade by Heber Bishop (The Bishop Collection; Metropolitan Museum of Art: New York).

Magic of Jewels and Charms by G. F. Kunz (New York, 1915).

Precious Stones of the Bible by C. W. Cooper (New York, 1924).

Quartz Family Minerals by H. C. Dake, et. al. (McGraw-Hill: New York, 1938).

Standard Dictionary of Folklore, Mythology & Legend (Funk and Wagnalls: New York, 1949).

WYNDHAM LIST OF

WEDDING ANNIVERSARY STONES

1st: Peridot *(from outer space)*
2nd: Garnet, red pyrope *(good cheer)*
3rd: Jade in rich colors, carved
(knowledge)
4th: Zircon, blue *(generosity)*
5th: Kunzite *(fair skies)*
6th: Turquoise, green *(safe travels)*
7th: Beryl, golden *(riches)*
8th: Tanzanite *(the newest, bluest gem)*
9th: Spinel, green *(peace)*
10th: Sapphire, blue *(tranquility)*

11th: Jacinth (yellow Zircon)
(mysteries of the East)
12th: Opal *(changing moods)*
13th: Hawk's-eye *(future foreseen)*
14th: Bloodstone quartz *(strong heart)*
15th: Alexandrite, green & red
(good fortune)
16th: Spinel, ruby red *(victory)*
17th: Carnelian, quartz *(bravery)*
18th: Aquamarine *(safety at sea)*
19th: Carbuncle (almandine garnet)
(Noah's floodlight)

20th:	Diamond, golden	*(wealth)*	
21st:	Tourmaline, red-violet	*(vigor)*	
22nd:	Sapphire, pink	*(magical power)*	
23rd:	Jade, green or blue jewels	*(power)*	
24th:	Hyacinth zircon	*(romance)*	
25th:	Garnet, green demantoid	*(joy)*	
26th:	Tigereye	*(a guard against evil)*	
27th:	Agate and Onyx quartz	*(willfulness)*	
28th:	Moonstone	*(mystery)*	
29th:	Topaz, blue	*(pure thoughts)*	
30th:	Pearl	*(faithfulness)*	
31st:	Amethyst	*(protection from wine)*	
32nd:	Morganite, pink beryl	*(long life)*	
33rd:	Garnet, star	*(passion)*	
34th:	Jasper quartz	*(rainmaker)*	
35th:	Emerald, green	*(health)*	
36th:	Topaz, clear	*(favor)*	
37th:	Chrysoberyl, chartreuse yellow	*(midsummer)*	
38th:	Sapphire, star	*(fame)*	
39th:	Zircon, blue	*(kindness)*	
40th:	Ruby, red	*(gem of the sun)*	
41st:	Jade, translucent white	*(wisdom)*	
42nd:	Turquoise, robin's egg (sky) blue	*(pride)*	
43rd:	Goshenite, clear beryl	*(insight)*	
44th:	Sardonyx quartz	*(dignity)*	
45th:	Cat's-eye beryl	*(forewarns against sorrow)*	
46th:	Spinel, golden	*(honor)*	
47th:	Diamond, pink	*(fearlessness)*	
48th:	Zircon, transparent	*(justice)*	
49th:	Sapphire, transparent	*(faith)*	
50th:	Topaz, golden	*(love)*	
55th:	Tourmaline, green	*(springtime)*	
60th:	Ruby, star	*(hope)*	
65th:	Spinel, blue	*(heaven's blessings)*	
70th:	Topaz, smokey brown	*(quiet)*	
75th:	Diamond, blue	*(spirit)*